# Soul Work

## A Workbook for Couples

*by*

Patrick J. McDonald, LSW, BCD

and Claudette M. McDonald, LSW, BCD

Paulist Press

*New York and Mahwah, NJ*

Book design by Nighthawk Design.



ISBN: 0-8091-3558-2

Published by Paulist Press
997 Macarthur Boulevard
Mahwah, New Jersey 07430

Printed and bound in the
United States of America

# *Introduction*

Greetings from both of us to both of you. This workbook is designed to help you improve the quality of your marriage. It is a companion to *The Soul of a Marriage.*

We recommend that you both read *The Soul of a Marriage* in its entirety before you begin. This will give you an overview of our thoughts on marital spirituality and prepare you to do the exercises.

The workbook is designed to be used in creative ways. It is an invitation to do soul work with one another. What we are inviting you to do is to explore, seek, question, pray, change and grow into the kind of shared soulfullness that is the gift of a rich marriage. To do soul work together is to discover the living God who brought you together and longs to create new life in you.

The exercises can be experienced a day at a time in a piecemeal fashion, incorporated into a day of reflection or used for a weekend retreat. You have the option to work your way through the workbook in a private setting or share your reflections with a group of couples, with the assistance of a group leader or retreat director.

There are no rules for the proper sequence of exercises. Some prefer to go from beginning to end in a systematic fashion, following the same development of thought as in *The Soul of a Marriage.* If this method does not meet your needs, we suggest you simply turn to a page that speaks to you and begin there. If the exercise is helpful, stay with it for as long as you wish. It is more important to savor the lessons of the moment than to push for completion.

Some exercises invite you to write about yourself.
Some ask that you share these thoughts with your spouse.
Some require quiet time and solitude.
Some ask you to pray together.

The directions are simple and straightforward. When the exercise indicates **INDIVIDUAL ASSIGNMENT,** do the exercise alone without consulting your spouse. When it calls for a **SHARED ASSIGNMENT,** spend the time as a couple: talking, sharing and working on the assignment together. Some specifically direct **HUSBAND** or **WIFE** to take the initiative.

We ask only that you bring an open mind, address your marriage with some optimism and learn to experience not only pleasant interaction, but the gracious love of God.

Feel free to be creative and flexible.
Feel free to innovate.
Feel free to grow with the moment.

Happy journeying to you both, and our thoughts are with you.

*Claudette and Patrick McDonald*

# *Section 1*

# So Your Marriage is Changing

## SHARED ASSIGNMENT

Read the first 34 pages of *The Soul of a Marriage* in order to get a flavor of how marriages change. We ask that both of you read the chapter, then remain silent for 15 minutes, allowing the experiences of the couples in the text to speak to you in a personal way. Ask yourselves if there are any similarities in your marriage to these stories.

## INDIVIDUAL ASSIGNMENT

Each of you find your private space, fill in the blanks for the following question without consulting one another.

## EXAMPLE

1. The change in my marriage that caught me most by surprise:
   "When he announced I was crowding him too much and he wanted to be left alone."

   How I dealt with the change:
   "I cried a lot, then tried to give him some space."

## NOW BEGIN

1. The change in my marriage that caught me most by surprise:

   How I dealt with the change:

2. The change in my marriage that brought the most joy:

   How I dealt with it:

3. The change in my marriage that was most painful:

   How I dealt with it:

4. The change in my marriage that turned out to be a blessing in disguise:

   How I dealt with the change:

5. The change in my marriage that opened the way to new freedom:

   How I dealt with it:

6. The change that I resisted for the longest time:

   How I decided to work it out:

7. The change that brought the greatest crisis to my marriage:

   How I met it:

8. The change in my marriage that was most welcome:

   How I welcomed it:

9. The part of my marriage that I most want to change now:

10. The part of my marriage that I least want to change now:

## SHARED ASSIGNMENT

Now that you have completed your answers, sit next to one another and share them. Spend some time discussing the different ways you view your marriage. Compare your similarities and differences. Try to appreciate your sameness as well as your uniqueness.

## INDIVIDUAL ASSIGNMENT

Now that you have listened to each other about your responses and shared the meaning of some changes, take about 10 minutes away from each other and rate your capacity to deal with change in your marriage:

Excellent ______

Good ______

Fair ______

Poor ______

Describe three reasons why you rated yourself as you did:

1.

2.

3.

Now rate your spouse's capacity to deal with change in the marriage:

Excellent ______

Good ______

Fair ______

Poor ______

Describe three reasons why you rated your spouse the way you did:

1.

2.

3.

## SHARED ASSIGNMENT

Take some time together to go through your answers, sharing the results. Listen to one another about how you see your problem-solving styles and capabilities. Share with each other your strengths and weaknesses. When you have listened to each other sufficiently, decide on three new methods you will bring to your marriage to deal with change and write them down.

1.

2.

3.

# *Section 2*

# Identifying Your Reactions

## INDIVIDUAL ASSIGNMENT

Find your separate spaces and read *The Soul of a Marriage* (pages 2–8). Try to comprehend how the six stages of change (shock and disbelief, denial, frustration, anger and depression, bargaining, generalized state of anxiety, the search for closure) reflect on your marriage.

## WRITE

1. Describe what major change in your marriage caused the greatest difficulty for you:

2. Write a brief diary of how the stages of change unfolded for you in the face of this major problem (remembering there are no right or wrong ways to undergo change):

3. Did the stages of change unfold in the same fashion as we described in *The Soul of a Marriage*? Describe what was similar and what was different.

## SHARED ASSIGNMENT

Come back together as a couple and share your answers. It is possible that you described different problems. You also might go through the stages of change differently from one another. Compare your answers to these questions and see what your differences are. The important thing is that you understand and learn to appreciate the different ways that you each problem-solve.

## SHARED ASSIGNMENT

Jointly decide three ways that you are going to support each other in problem-solving in your marriage from this day forward:

1.

2.

3.

# *Section 3*

# Understanding the Differences in Men and Women

**INDIVIDUAL ASSIGNMENT**

Take your separate spaces and read pages 8–13 from *The Soul of a Marriage.* Note the sections of the text that describe some of the differences in the ways that men and women deal with problem-solving. Below is a sample question concerning the differences in style. After you have read the example, proceed to the exercise below, and answer the questions about the differences in process for you and your spouse.

**EXAMPLE**

1. Describe in detail the most complicated *interpersonal* problem you have ever struggled with as a couple:
   "Understanding that we are not the same persons, that I must talk and problem-solve out loud or I feel left out of his life."
2. Describe the outcome:
   "We were badly out of phase with one another for months, until it became a crisis and I confronted it."

**WRITE**

1. Describe in detail the most complicated *interpersonal* problem you have ever struggled with as a couple:

2. Describe the outcome:

3. Describe the process that led to the resolution of the problem:

4. Describe what made the decision difficult for you:

5. What differences became apparent concerning the ways that you and your spouse relate to the problem-solving process?

## SHARED ASSIGNMENT

Come back together as a couple. Discuss what you defined as a difficult interpersonal problem. Discuss how you each addressed your problem. Now compare and contrast the differences in how you went about your processes.

## SHARED ASSIGNMENT

1. List five real ways that your problem-solving processes differed for you as a man or woman:

| Husband | Wife |
| --- | --- |
| 1. ______________ | 1. ______________ |
| 2. ______________ | 2. ______________ |
| 3. ______________ | 3. ______________ |
| 4. ______________ | 4. ______________ |
| 5. ______________ | 5. ______________ |

2. What lessons did you learn about how much alike or how different you are?

3. Describe three ways that these differences will be dealt with in your future problem-solving in the marriage:

   (a)

   (b)

   (c)

# Section 4

# Togetherness and Individuality

## INDIVIDUAL ASSIGNMENT

Take your separate spaces and read pages 14–22 in *The Soul of a Marriage* concerning the experiences of togetherness and individuality. Take all the time necessary to reflect on how the flow of energy affects your marriage. Now respond to the following questions:

1. Togetherness most often means to me:

2. The riskiest moments of togetherness for me are:

3. The deepest hunger for togetherness comes for me when:

4. The most memorable time of togetherness for me was:

5. The richest rewards of togetherness for me are:

6. Individuality most often means to me:

7. The richest moment of individuality for me comes when:

8. The deepest hunger for individuality comes when:

9. The most memorable experience of individuality for me was:

10. The richest rewards of individuality for me are:

## SHARED ASSIGNMENT

Come back together as a couple and share the results of your reflection. Compare what you learned about your similarities and differences. Determine how these differences contribute to a richer life together. Discuss how these differences have led to hurt and emptiness. Finally, write out *together* your responses to the following directives:

1. Agree on three ways that you will respect each other's need for individuality.

   (a)

   (b)

   (c)

2. Agree on three ways that you will move toward a renewed effort at togetherness:

   (a)

   (b)

   (c)

# Section 5

## Plotting Your Positions

### INDIVIDUAL ASSIGNMENT

Find your private space again. If you need to refresh your mind about the central role of togetherness and individuality in explaining how marriages work, read *The Soul of a Marriage,* pages 14–22. Think about this phrase which is rather common for a marriage, "When I'm tired, I just like to be left alone." This is a statement of individuality, spoken when a person feels tired. Individuality and togetherness can be visually represented as two poles, encompassing a broad range of behaviors:

Togetherness ____________________________________________ Individuality

The statement, "When I'm tired I just like to be left alone," can be represented by an X in a position near the pole of individuality. The X visually represents where this individual wants to be for a time: left alone with tiredness.

Togetherness ____________________________________ X ______ Individuality

Making an X at this end of the spectrum would be in stark contrast to what a spouse might desire in order to deal with the same tiredness. In that case, a spouse might say, "When I'm tired I like to be held." That can be visually represented on the togetherness versus individuality scale in this fashion:

Togetherness ______ O____________________________________ Individuality

The two positions of individuality or togetherness represent an *emotional resolution* for the matter of tiredness. In other words, when a person feels tired, the tension is relieved by being left alone or by being held and nurtured. Either way, a person feels better. The emotional resolutions would look something like these examples, if the positions of togetherness or individuality were defined in more concrete ways:

## EXAMPLE

Togetherness ________________ X ________________ Individuality

| | |
|---|---|
| I want to be held | I want to be left alone |
| I want to be nurtured | I desire to be forgotten |
| I love to be embraced | Don't touch me |

Explanation: "Sometimes I desire to be held when I really feel insecure. At other times when I'm tired and angry at the same time, I want my space."

In this case, the X is placed on the line midway between togetherness and individuality. The X represents where this person is emotionally, what sort of space or closeness might be desired and what kind of response is sought from a spouse. The more clearly spouses speak to one another about what they want during changing emotional states, the easier it is for them to relate to one another.

## WRITE

Take a pencil and make an X on the line for each of the following emotional states. To help you, we have made the positions of togetherness and individuality very concrete. As in the example above, there is a space for you to offer more details about your position if you wish. Feel free to mark up your workbook in any way you want in order to clarify how you position yourself as your emotional needs change.

1. "When I'm tired."

Togetherness ________________________________________________ Individuality

| | |
|---|---|
| I love to be held | I want to be alone |
| I want to be nurtured | I want my independence |
| I want to be talked to | I love quiet time |

Explanation:

2. "When I'm hurt."

| Togetherness ________________ | Individuality |
|---|---|
| I want to be cared for | I want to be alone |
| I need to be soothed | I need space |
| I crave love and caring | I nurse my own wounds |

Explanation:

3. "When I'm angry."

| Togetherness ________________ | Individuality |
|---|---|
| I get it out | I keep it in |
| I want to be heard | I crave quiet |
| I need to process | I want to think |

Explanation:

4. "When I'm anxious."

| Togetherness ________________ | Individuality |
|---|---|
| I express it | I don't talk |
| I do things together | I go it alone |
| I need help | I need nothing |

Explanation:

5. "When I'm lonely."

| Togetherness ________________ | Individuality |
|---|---|
| I like to talk | I love solitude |
| I need a suggestion | I'll figure it out |
| I love interaction | I like quiet |

Explanation:

6. "When I'm empty."

| Togetherness ________________ | Individuality |
|---|---|
| I need to be filled | I need alone time |
| I love company | I feel it alone |
| I must talk | I must be alone |

Explanation:

7. "When I'm happy."

| Togetherness ________________ | Individuality |
|---|---|
| I can't wait to share | I hold it in |
| I'm expansive | I withdraw |
| I spread the joy | I keep it in |

Explanation:

8. "When I'm moody."

| Togetherness | Individuality |
|---|---|
| I share it | I keep it quiet |
| I pursue answers | I ignore contact |
| I need to be comforted | I am not interested |

Explanation:

9. "When I'm jealous."

| Togetherness | Individuality |
|---|---|
| I need to confront | I'm more passive |
| I blame someone else | I ignore it |
| I lose it | I keep it in |

Explanation:

10. "When I'm threatened."

| Togetherness | Individuality |
|---|---|
| I bring it up | I ignore it |
| I confront it | I deny it |
| I solve it jointly | I solve it myself |

Explanation:

11. "When I'm sad."

| Togetherness ________________ | Individuality |
|---|---|
| We cry together | I cry alone |
| I share the feelings | I carry them |
| I ask for comfort | I want space |

Explanation:

12. "When I'm confused."

| Togetherness ________________ | Individuality |
|---|---|
| I ask for dialogue | I keep it quiet |
| I process it with my beloved | I think it through, alone |
| I own it | I deny it |

Explanation:

13. "When I'm competitive."

| Togetherness ________________ | Individuality |
|---|---|
| I own it | I go for it |
| I soften | I don't give away my position |
| I compromise | Nothing doing |

Explanation:

14. "When I'm insecure."

| Togetherness | Individuality |
|---|---|
| I admit it | I deny it |
| I ask for support | I overcome it alone |
| I invite talk | I go it alone |

Explanation:

15. "When I'm alienated."

| Togetherness | Individuality |
|---|---|
| I admit it | I bear it |
| I ask for help | No way! |
| I explore the relationship | I look elsewhere |

Explanation:

16. "When I'm resentful."

| Togetherness | Individuality |
|---|---|
| I admit it | I carry it |
| I confront my spouse | I stay distant |
| I name the resentments | I hold grudges |

Explanation:

17. "When I'm eager."

| Togetherness ________________ | Individuality |
|---|---|
| I seek out my spouse | I keep it quiet |
| I talk openly | I calculate quietly |
| I dream out loud | I exercise caution |

Explanation:

18. "When I'm frightened."

| Togetherness ________________ | Individuality |
|---|---|
| I ask for support | I face it alone |
| I explore it | I withdraw |
| I face it jointly | I go it alone |

Explanation:

We know that we cannot cover every emotional state that is important to you, so we now offer two spaces for you that are open ended. Follow the same procedure, use your creativity, and fill in the blanks as you choose.

19. "When I'm ____________."

| Togetherness ________________ | Individuality |
|---|---|
| ____________ | ____________ |
| ____________ | ____________ |
| ____________ | ____________ |

Explanation:

20. "When I'm ______________________."

    Togetherness ______________________________________________ Individuality

    ______________________________ ______________________________

    ______________________________ ______________________________

    ______________________________ ______________________________

    Explanation:

Now that you have completed this segment of the workbook, try one more variation. Go back to number 1 and instead of plotting your own position on the scale of togetherness versus individuality, plot your spouse. Use the letter O instead of an X, so you can keep them straight.

## EXAMPLE

1. "When I'm tired." (O=spouse X=self)

    Togetherness ______ X __________ O __________________________ Individuality

    | | |
    |---|---|
    | I want to be held | I want to be left alone |
    | I want to be nurtured | I desire to be forgotten |
    | I love to be embraced | Don't touch me |

    Explanation:

    "When I'm tired, I like to be held and loved. It makes me secure. When my spouse feels tired I don't know what to do. Should I offer comfort and consolation? Should I get out of the way? I need more information."

## SHARED ASSIGNMENT

Go back to sharing as a couple and sort through your responses. Talk in depth about how your emotional states are expressed in positions of togetherness or individuality. Compare the ways that you see each other and share where the differences and likenesses are. Answer the following questions, *jointly:*

1. What did you learn about the ways that you each deal with emotions?

2. Select three ways that you are going to respect each other's process from here on:

   (a)

   (b)

   (c)

3. Each of you define where you are *most of the time* on the togetherness versus individuality scale:

4. Describe several ways that these positions benefit your marriage:

5. Select one critical area where you need more balance:

6. Decide on one goal to move you toward that balance:

# *Section 6*

# Moving Toward a Balance

## INDIVIDUAL ASSIGNMENT

Xerox pages 22–25 and scotch tape them together in order to form one long profile, making sure you keep the pages in their proper sequence. Now take note of several things:

1. The top and bottom of the scale are identical to the scale of togetherness and individuality you worked with in section 5.
2. The major portion of the scale is made up of a series of expressions we often hear from spouses as they struggle for individuality and togetherness. Each phrase is marked with an X. If you look up or down, you can see that the X locates the phrase somewhere along the scale of togetherness vs. individuality, just like you did for yourself in section 5.
3. The black boxes represent key positions in a marriage as it changes from **TIGHT TOGETHERNESS** to **DEEPENING INDIVIDUALITY** to **CRYSTALLIZED INDIVIDUALITY** to an **INTEGRATED MARRIAGE**
4. The little arrows simply represent the ways that energy flows in a marriage from individuality to togetherness etc., as it changes.

## INDIVIDUAL ASSIGNMENT

Now take a pencil and put a circle around the X in front of each phrase that represents an expression of your position in the marriage right now.

**Togetherness** ________________________________________________ Individuality

**TIGHT TOGETHERNESS** ◄◄ ◄◄◄◄◄ **ENERGY FLOW** ◄◄◄

X—I can't live without her.

X—We are really the same.

X—We think the same, we feel the same.

X—Only closeness matters.

X—He makes all the real decisions.

X—I'm head of the house.

X—Our differences are only surface.

X—I feel guilty about change.

X—If I lost her, I'd just die.

X—I don't trust my own decisions.

X—I'm only alive when we're together.

X—We'll never be separated.

X—When I argue, I really feel guilty.

X—If I don't hang on tight, she'll be gone

X—When he hurts, I hurt more.

X—She dominates all my thoughts and feelings.

**AREA OF BEGINNING INDIVIDUALITY ➤➤ ENERGY FLOW ➤➤➤**

X—Sometimes I love him, sometimes I hate him.

X—I long for the single life again.

X—No one really understands me.

X—I really find it hard to trust him.

X—I'm not budging.

X—The only time we're close is after a fight.

X—I'm beginning to identify my feelings.

**AREA OF DEVELOPING INDIVIDUALITY ➤➤➤➤➤➤➤➤➤➤➤➤➤➤➤➤➤➤**

X—I'm confused about what I want.

X—I'm very disappointed in marriage.

X—My life would be happy if not for her.

X—I'm angry and hurt

X—Every time we talk, we fight.

X—I feel strong until he disapproves.

X—I don't want you to parent me.

X—I'm learning to speak for myself.

X—I feel empty most of the time.

X—Nothing is ever good enough.

X—I'm angry at the mere mention of compromise.

X—I feel betrayed.

X—I want closeness, but hate it.

**AREA OF DEEPENING INDIVIDUALITY ➤➤➤➤➤➤➤➤➤➤➤**

X—I know my needs like I never have.

X—I won't place myself in a secondary position any more.

X—I want closeness but hate it.

X—I miss her when she's gone, but hate her when she's around.

X—I feel good about speaking my mind.

**AREA OF CRYSTALLIZED INDIVIDUALITY ➤➤➤➤➤➤➤➤➤➤➤➤**

X—I will continue to direct my own life, thank you. I do not want your help.

X—I know what I want and I'm clear about it.

X—No one is going to control me! Ever!

X—I'm angry at you all the time.

X—My life goes on, no matter what.

X—You are not going to define how I think and feel.

X—My emotions will no longer govern my life.

**ENERGY FLOW ➤➤➤➤➤➤➤➤➤➤➤➤➤➤➤➤➤➤➤➤➤➤➤➤**

X—I know what I want and I'm clear about it.

X—I'm changing, whether he likes it or not.

X—Get out of my way. I hate you.

**◀◀◀◀◀◀◀◀◀◀◀◀ ENERGY FLOW TOWARD INTEGRATED TOGETHERNESS**

X—I've learned to appreciate who he is.

X—I'm ready to re-evaluate the marriage.

X—I've found myself, so I don't fear losing my identity.

X—I'm not fearful of being engulfed.

X—More and more I say, live and let live.

X—We are not the same persons, and never will be.

X—I am responsible for my own actions.

X—The only person who can make me happy, is me!

X—I think change is good for us.

X—I'm lightening up, and learning to appreciate myself.

**◄◄◄ MOVES TOWARD AN INTEGRATED MARRIAGE ◄◄◄◄◄◄**

X—I'm learning to appreciate myself.
X—I feel positive about my own experiences.
X—I'm comfortable with my own sexuality.
X—I wouldn't trade life with anyone.
X—I believe fighting in marriage is very healthy.

X—I have my own life and really enjoy it.

X—I don't expect her to make me happy.

X—I trust my own decisions.

**◄◄◄◄◄◄◄ STRONG PULL TOWARD INTEGRATED MARRIAGE ◄◄◄◄**

X—Trust and respect for one another go together.
X—I don't expect her to make me me happy.

X—Being together and being quiet, is communication.

X—I like being nurtured and expect it.

X—When I feel vulnerable I feel safe.
X—I can dream my dreams with her.
X—We can balance it all out: intimacy and separateness.

X—I can make sacrifices if I must.
X—I enjoy sharing openly with her.

X—Our differences no longer divide us.
X—I know what to expect.
X—First and foremost, marriage is teamwork.

X—We really respect and affirm each other's dreams.

X—I enjoy the daily routine of marriage.

X—Some things I can change, some things I live with, but it's O.K.

X—I feel in touch with him most of the time.

**Togetherness** ________________________________________ Individuality

## SHARED ASSIGNMENT

1. Look at the Xes you circled on the scale. How did they cluster for you? Or not cluster?

2. Share with your partner what the clustering is saying to each of you about:

   (a) The movement in your marriage toward individuality or togetherness.

   (b) Are your respective positions a source of unity or divisiveness?

   (c) What do you desire in a healthy balance between togetherness and individuality?

3. Set three practical goals for yourselves about how you will work for a more satisfactory balance in your marriage.

# Section 7

## Seeking the Face of a Spirituality

### INDIVIDUAL ASSIGNMENT

Take your separate spaces and read pages 23–27 in *The Soul of a Marriage.* This section describes the three faces of marital spirituality. Now answer the following questions:

1. What is the face of your marital spirituality?

2. Are you content with this model?

3. If not, what changes do you wish to make?

### SHARED ASSIGNMENT

Find your spouse and share your responses with one another. Digest what your similarities and differences are. Decide how you are going to relate to your proposed changes.

# Section 8

## Setting the Foundations for a Spirituality

### INDIVIDUAL ASSIGNMENT

Read pages 26–43 of *The Soul of a Marriage.* Do some reflecting on each of the foundational elements for a spirituality and try to comprehend how some or all apply to you. Reflect especially on the notion of a *shared* spirituality as the central component of development. You will find below the same scale of togetherness versus individuality and by now have some familiarity with the way energy flows between the two forces.

We want you to begin reflecting on marital spirituality as an expression of these two forces as well. Take each phrase listed below, and plot the same X for yourself to express where you are between togetherness and individuality. Here is an example:

"When I pray."

| Togetherness ____________________ | X | ____________________ Individuality |
|---|---|---|
| I want to pray together | | I pray alone |
| I enjoy holding hands | | I prefer not to |
| I love deep sharing | | I'm uncomfortable |

Explanation:

"For the most part, I believe praying is rather private. But there are times when I'll do it your way because I know you enjoy it."

### WRITE

Take each of the following phrases about how togetherness and individuality relate to a spirituality and profile yourself by placing an X in the proper location. If an explanation is needed, write one:

1. "When I pray."

| Togetherness ________ | Individuality |
|---|---|
| I want to pray together | I pray alone |
| I enjoy holding hands | I prefer not to |
| I love deep sharing | I'm uncomfortable |

Explanation:

2. "When I read the scriptures."

| Togetherness ________ | Individuality |
|---|---|
| I love reflecting together | I prefer alone |
| I love deep sharing | I don't like it |
| I am inclusive | I'm exclusive |

Explanation:

3. "When I attend liturgies."

| Togetherness ________ | Individuality |
|---|---|
| We participate jointly | I participate alone |
| I love to share the benefits | I keep quiet |
| I feel close | I don't feel close |

Explanation:

4. "When I do ministry projects."

| Togetherness ____________________ | Individuality |
|---|---|
| It is always together | I prefer alone |
| We share the joys | I keep it quiet |
| Sharing is primary | Goals count |

Explanation:

5. "When I seek quiet time."

| Togetherness ____________________ | Individuality |
|---|---|
| Together but alone | Solely alone |
| We share the quiet | No sharing |
| We are open to talk | I keep quiet |

Explanation:

6. "When I make a retreat."

| Togetherness ____________________ | Individuality |
|---|---|
| I prefer to share it | I'd rather be alone |
| I love dialogue and sharing | I prefer quiet |
| Couple-oriented | Individually oriented |

Explanation:

7. "When I reflect on the presence of God."

| Togetherness ________ | Individuality |
|---|---|
| I love the sharing | Prefer solitary time |
| Related to our process | Unrelated |
| Shared feelings | No feelings |

Explanation:

8. "When I learn more about spirituality."

| Togetherness ________ | Individuality |
|---|---|
| I prefer sharing | I prefer to do it alone |
| I love the process | I tolerate it |
| I exchange ideas | I keep them quiet |

Explanation:

9. "When I define what marital spirituality is."

| Togetherness ________ | Individuality |
|---|---|
| The process is central | Process means nothing |
| Always includes spouse | Sometimes |
| Heals the marriage | Secondary matter |

Explanation:

10. "Reaching out to others."

| Togetherness ______ | Individuality |
|---|---|
| Always together | Alone |
| Enriches our marriage | Secondary matter |
| Essential for our growth | An intrusion |

Explanation:

11. "Our changing images of God."

| Togetherness ______ | Individuality |
|---|---|
| Nurturer | Ruler |
| Lover | Law Giver |
| She | He |
| Mother | Father |
| Inclusive | Exclusive |

Explanation:

Now that you have located yourself within these scales, locate your spouse with an O, in the same fashion as you did with the previous scales on emotional resolution.

Togetherness __________ X _____________ O _________________________ Individuality

## SHARED ASSIGNMENT

Share with your spouse the ways that you profiled yourself and each other. Talk openly about what you learned.

## WRITE

1. Set three priorities about how you are going to grow in your marital spirituality in the next year:

   (a)

   (b)

   (c)

# Section 9

# Spirituality as Meaning

## INDIVIDUAL ASSIGNMENT

Take some private time and fill in the answers:

1. What was the most difficult experience you endured last year?

2. How did your spirituality give meaning to the experience?

3. Was it lacking?

4. Where do you need to deepen your spirituality and what kind of emphasis might have helped you?

## SHARED ASSIGNMENT

Share your answers with your spouse to see where your similarities and differences are. Compare what you have learned.

**WIFE:** Read this section of the gospel of St. John to your spouse. Listen closely to the message for your marriage:

> I am the true vine,
> and my Father is the vinedresser.
> Every branch in me that bears no fruit
> he cuts away,
> and every branch that does bear fruit he prunes
> to make it bear even more.
> You are pruned already,
> by means of the word that I have spoken to you.
> Make your home in me, as I make mine in you.
> As a branch cannot bear fruit all by itself,
> but must remain a part of the vine,
> neither can you unless you remain in me.
> I am the vine,
> you are the branches.
> Whoever remains in me, with me in them,
> bears fruit in plenty;
> for cut off from me you can do nothing.
> Anyone who does not remain in me
> is like a branch that has been thrown away
> —it withers;
> these branches are collected and thrown into the
> fire, and they are burnt.
> If you remain in me
> and my words remain in you,
> you may ask what you will
> and you shall get it.

## SHARED ASSIGNMENT

Sit silently for a time and let the scriptures speak to you of the connection between yourself, your spouse and God. How does it speak to you about finding a deeper soulfullness for your lives? What would you like to ask God for now, believing that God will grant it?

## SHARED ASSIGNMENT

Try to pray aloud together and ask God to give you what you need for a richer life together. Ask God to bond you together more deeply in prayer. Also ask God to help you find a sense of the sacred in the everyday events of your life.

# Section 10

## Setting Your Priorities

### INDIVIDUAL ASSIGNMENT

Find some quiet space and read pages 31–32 in *The Soul of a Marriage.* Fill in the responses to the following tasks.

1. Describe the main priority in your life:

2. Rank in the order of importance the three most important priorities in your marriage:

   (a)

   (b)

   (c)

3. If you are ready to make the development of a spirituality the main priority in your marriage, what needs to be changed?

4. List several ways you are going to create enough space in your marriage to make this a priority:

### SHARED ASSIGNMENT

Share the responses to these questions with one another. Share what your similarities and differences are. Now jointly decide what you want to rearrange for your life.

# Section 11

# Respecting Each Other's Processes

## INDIVIDUAL ASSIGNMENT

Find a quiet space and read pages 32–33 of *The Soul of a Marriage.* Take note of the information concerning the different ways that men and women relate to marital spirituality. Now answer the following questions.

1. Describe several ways that your spouse differs from you

   (a) in the ways of prayer:

   (b) in the ways of imaging God:

   (c) in the ways of living a spirituality:

2. Describe the ways that you and your spouse have reflected upon the changing roles of men and women and how it has influenced your marriage:

3. Describe how your experiences of loving (as man and as woman) have changed your understanding of God's ways of loving:

4. Describe three significant ways that your different experiences of love have helped you grow:

   (a)

   (b)

   (c)

5. Describe three ways that your different experiences have made your growth difficult:

   (a)

   (b)

   (c)

## SHARED ASSIGNMENT

Find your spouse and share your answers. Spend some time reflecting upon the different ways that you deal with questions of spirituality. Relate jointly to the following mandate.

1. Construct one resolution where you are going to go about your spirituality more attuned to each other's processes:

# Section 12

## Opening to the Love of God

### SHARED ASSIGNMENT

Read together pages 33–35 from *The Soul of a Marriage.* These experiences of coming to an awareness of God in a marriage are perhaps no different from your own, if you take the time to listen for the voice of God. As the book states, it is our belief that every couple is called to a deep union with God. Your task is to get "in touch" with what is already going on within you. Take turns sharing with one another three experiences:

1. Describe to your spouse one experience whereby you became aware of the love of God in your marriage:

2. Share with your spouse how you experience God on a day-to-day basis in your marriage:

3. What would you like to open up in your marriage, in order to know God's love more genuinely?

Now write out three goals for yourselves that are aimed at finding God in your lives:

(a)

(b)

(c)

# Section 13

## Cultivating a Sense of Gratitude

**SHARED ASSIGNMENT**

Sit together as a couple and read pages 35–36 from *The Soul of a Marriage* about the nature of gratitude. Be quiet and let the sense of gratitude for all the great gifts that you have been given begin to sink in. Now share the following questions:

1. Describe the event in your marriage that began to open up a sense of gratitude:

2. Describe the gift for which you are most grateful in your marriage:

3. Share where you believe you lack gratitude at times:

# Section 14

# Confronting the Darkness

## SHARED ASSIGNMENT

Take time together as a couple and take turns reading to one another pages 36–43 in *The Soul of a Marriage.* Read it slowly, while trying to understand the central notion of darkness. Stay quiet for a time and begin to reflect upon the various darknesses you have already encountered in your marriage:

changing expectations for one another;
difficult news;
deep losses;
financial difficulties;
hurt inflicted in moments of anger;
harsh words you want to take back;
knowing your own dark shadows.

## SHARED ASSIGNMENT

1. Describe for one another a darkness that was especially difficult for your marriage:

2. Did the darkness lead to a different experience of God for one or both of you?

3. Explain how your experience changed your awareness of God (include your current questions and concerns):

4. How have these changes affected your marriage?

## SHARED ASSIGNMENT

Be quiet in the presence of one another. Become aware that you are reflecting on what the great contemplative authors have told us about God dwelling in the darkness of change. Spend a few moments just quieting down and breathing deeply while you slowly repeat the words of the psalmist to yourself, "Be still and know that I am God." Reflect on a current problem between the two of you and ask God to sustain, enlighten and deepen your marriage as you move through the darkness, seeking the light. Stay quiet for about 15 minutes and let God speak to you about several matters:

1. God loves you unconditionally as a couple.
2. God has your best interests in mind.
3. God gives life and sustains it.
4. God brings light out of the darkness.
5. God loves you to wholeness as long as you are open to it.

## SHARED ASSIGNMENT

Simply share with one another:

1. What is your most loved image of God? (example: God is Father, God is Beloved, God is Mother, God is compassionate love.)

2. Where are you in relationship to God at this moment of your history?

3. Is God more real or less real than when you first met one another?

4. Is God present to you in your marriage and if so, in what way?

5. How does God's presence in your lives differ from your early days of marriage?

6. Do you continue to experience God's love even though changes have taken place in your marriage?

7. Do you want God to become more real in your marriage?

8. Get practical and list three ways that you will work to make God more real for your marriage:

   (a)

   (b)

   (c)

# Section 15

## The Stages of Marriage

### INDIVIDUAL ASSIGNMENT

Find some quiet space and read pages 44–108 from *The Soul of a Marriage* about the life of a marriage. This will give you a feel for how marriages change over time. Reflect on the discussion of stages in the book, then realize that not every person is expected to move through these stages in the same way. Some couples may only touch on the changes described. Others may be fixed in one stage and be comfortable with it. There is no right or wrong way to experience them.

Feel free to go to a stage of marriage that relates to your experiences. Spend a few minutes simply assessing where you are in your marriage. Because of the sensitive nature of some of these exercises, you may or may not find them inviting. If not, don't feel guilty. You may prefer quiet time, just to be with God, your spouse, or yourself.

# Section 16

## Early Marriage

### INDIVIDUAL ASSIGNMENT

Find some quiet space and read to yourself pages 48–53 from *The Soul of a Marriage.* Listen to what the text tells you about early marriage and feel good if you are in that stage. Write out your responses to the following questions.

1. Describe what is a genuine feeling of closeness in your marriage:

2. I feel most like communicating with my spouse when:

3. I feel least like communicating with my spouse when:

4. Describe some of the ways that sex and love are interrelated in your marriage:

5. Describe some ways that sex has become of greater or lesser importance since you have been married:

6. My idea of freedom in marriage is:

7. My spouse's idea of freedom is:

## SHARED ASSIGNMENT

Find your spouse, sit down together, and compare your answers. Discuss your similarities and differences.

## SHARED ASSIGNMENT

**HUSBAND:** Read *Morning Encounter* (page 52) from *The Soul of a Marriage* to your wife. Read it to her in a slow, romantic fashion, letting the words sink into your hearts. Be quiet for a few moments.

**HUSBAND:** Describe for your wife three ways that you plan to construct a more comfortable kind of intimacy with her:

1.

2.

3.

**WIFE:** Write a brief description about how you feel about what your husband has written:

## SHARED ASSIGNMENT

**WIFE:** Turn to pages 52–53 of *The Soul of a Marriage* and find *First Anniversary: Prayer of Gratitude from Her.* Read it slowly and lovingly to your husband. Let the words sink into your hearts.

**WIFE:** Take a few moments and list the three gifts in your marriage for which you are most grateful:

1.

2.

3.

**HUSBAND:** List the three gifts for which you are most grateful:

1.

2.

3.

# *Section 17*

# Clouds on the Horizon

## INDIVIDUAL ASSIGNMENT

Find a quiet space and read pages 54–63 from *The Soul of a Marriage.* Let it speak to you about the beginning process of change and how it influences a marital spirituality. Now fill in the following questions.

1. Describe several instances when your spouse demonstrated genuine love to you during the last month:

2. Describe several situations in which you, intentionally or unintentionally, were hurtful to your spouse in the last month:

3. Describe the ways that you and your spouse are different:

4. What are the strengths that you bring to your marriage?

5. What are the strengths that your spouse brings to your marriage?

6. How do you use your strong points to grow in your marriage?

7. What are the weaknesses you bring to your marriage?

8. What are some of your spouse's weaknesses?

## SHARED ASSIGNMENT

Share the results of the questions with your spouse and decide where you find the likenesses and differences. Discuss them. Set three goals you want to achieve for your marriage to help you affirm each other's strengths.

1.

2.

3.

## SHARED ASSIGNMENT

Read together: *In the Aftermath: A Prayer for Both* (pages 61–62 of *The Soul of a Marriage*). After you have recited this prayer together, sit quietly and let the presence of God become real for you. If you so desire, you can read the other prayers and poems that are in the same section of *The Soul of a Marriage.*

# Section 18

## Divorce and Remarriage

### INDIVIDUAL ASSIGNMENT

Find your separate space and reflect on the fact that you have entered into another marriage. Your transition has brought with it all the risks and joys of starting over again with another person. You know that the journey has not been an easy one, and that there are more obstacles ahead. You are probably also aware of some very real fears you carry about success or failure.

Read *Second Marriage: Accountability* (*The Soul of a Marriage,* page 89) to yourself. Sit quietly and absorb the atmosphere created by this prayer. Write your responses to the following questions:

1. Write a brief description of the ways that you have mourned the death of your previous marriage:

2. Describe the ways that you are still in the mourning process:

3. Describe three gifts that this mourning process has brought you:

   (a)

   (b)

   (c)

4. Describe several fears about success and failure you bring with you into this new marriage:

## SHARED ASSIGNMENT

Find your spouse and share what you have written, taking the time to understand one another. Give yourself plenty of time to share the feelings that are a part of the difficult task of beginning another marriage and making it work. When you have finished discussing your answers, work together to respond to the following:

1. Describe three practical ways you are going to be supportive to one another as you move into this marriage:

   (a)

   (b)

   (c)

2. Develop strategies about how you are going to jointly deal with former spouses in the following areas:

   (a) around holiday stresses:

   (b) when you meet by accident:

   (c) when your private space is invaded by a former spouse:

   (d) when you are asked to make decisions that are outside the divorce decree:

## SHARED ASSIGNMENT

Read together *Second Marriage: Accountability* (*The Soul of a Marriage,* page 89) and discuss its implications for your situation. Be open with each other about the difficult areas you are called upon to face. Name the dark shadows described in the prayer that are especially frightening, and ask each other for support. Jointly develop a response to the following:

1. Describe the shadows that are especially burdensome to you:

2. What are your shadows teaching you about yourself and your need to grow?

3. Describe what shadows you are now ready to surrender to God's guidance, enlightenment and care:

## SHARED ASSIGNMENT

Decide who will read. Read the following prayer to one another on behalf of the marriage:

God of all healing and love.
We come before you,
unsure of the demands of our own love.
Questioning our direction for the future
and what you ask of us.
The shadows of what we want to deny
can no longer remain hidden.
They call us to an honest exchange at last.
Be with us, loving God.
Let us respond to the challenge of love.
We either surrender or we die as a couple.
Give us the strength, the honesty, the words,
to let go of all that keeps us
from loving one another and knowing You.
Strengthen us to face the parts of ourselves
that we resist knowing.
Heal us in the depths where the pain we carry
has never been disclosed.
Move through our relationship
as a peaceful wave of love and security.
Sustain us through the dark journey.
Carry us into the light of a cleansed and healed love.
Deepen our care for one another even as we pray.
Do not let our fears send us back to the
shadows of our emptiness.
Give us the great gifts of peace and confidence
that come from knowing that all love
comes from you
is sustained by you
and is blessed by you.

# *Section 19*

# Blended Family

## INDIVIDUAL ASSIGNMENT

Find some private space and read to yourself *Blended Family* (*The Soul of a Marriage,* page 88). Allow the experiences associated with blending families to come into your awareness. Do not hesitate to become aware of the joys as well as the pain associated with this difficult work. Respond to the following:

1. Describe three experiences about blending your family that have been joyful:

   (a)

   (b)

   (c)

2. Describe three experiences about blending your family that have been painful:

   (a)

   (b)

   (c)

3. Describe several tasks that still need to be accomplished in order to make your family atmosphere more livable and harmonious:

## SHARED ASSIGNMENT

Come together as a couple and share the responses to your questions. Take plenty of time to share the joys as well as the difficulties related to blending your family. Pull together what you have shared in the following exercise.

1. Agree upon and define three concrete goals that will make your family more livable and harmonious:

   (a)

   (b)

   (c)

## INDIVIDUAL ASSIGNMENT

Take some private space again and each of you read *Conversation with God Over Coffee: Alone* (*The Soul of a Marriage,* pages 69–70). Spend some time thinking about where there is room in your marriage to surrender and where there is a need to be clear and straightforward about your beliefs. Relate to these questions:

1. Describe three experiences that have disappointed you about attempting to blend two families:

   (a)

   (b)

   (c)

2. Identify two areas where you are ready to surrender the whole matter to God:

   (a)

   (b)

3. Identify two areas where you will not give away your integrity:

   (a)

   (b)

## SHARED ASSIGNMENT

Come back together as a couple and share your responses. Spend a lot of time weighing the options about what you want from each other. Jointly respond:

1. Describe the ways that you will work to achieve a balance between surrender and authenticity in the work of blending your families:

2. Describe some ways that you will be supportive to one another as you make this new family experience work:

# Section 20

# Learning to Let Go

**SHARED ASSIGNMENT**

Find a personal space and read pages 64–72 from *The Soul of a Marriage.* After you have reflected for a time on the material in the book, answer the following questions for yourself:

1. What in my marriage has presented the most difficult task of letting go?

2. Describe a pleasant surprise that came to you from finally letting go:

3. Describe several ways that letting go has been beneficial to your marriage:

4. Have you found any sense of the presence of God by letting go? If so, how?

**SHARED ASSIGNMENT**

Come together as a couple and share your responses to the questions. Compare your likenesses and differences and share how they have helped or hindered you in your quest for a spirituality.

## SHARED ASSIGNMENT

Read together: *In Response to the Call of Love: For Both* (*The Soul of a Marriage,* page 70). Be silent for a time and allow the prayer to speak to you. Begin to image God as the source of all love. God's deep compassion calls you to a renewal of love for one another. Allow the presence of the compassionate God to touch you deeply in order to grow into a more mature love.

## SHARED ASSIGNMENT

Take turns reading the following prayer to one another while you hold hands (save one hand, however, to hold the workbook):

God of compassionate love.
We come to you in all honesty.
Open our hearts to love.
Open our minds to see who you really are.
Bring our love to maturity.
Let us experience the gentle touch of your care for us.
You are the God of healing love.
Give us patience when we need it.
Give us a grounding when we lack it.
Give us compassion when we become hardened.
Give us staying power when we weaken.
Let us come to accept
that we must go through our own letting go
of everything that is not genuine
in order to know and love one another.
Let our love reflect your deep compassion.
May we be tempered by our trials.
May we see that even in the darkness
you are present and real,
and will always journey with us.

# Section 21

## Focus on Forgiveness

*Note:* Focus on forgiveness can be repeated in any number of places throughout this workbook. Any stage of development brings its unique challenges of forgiveness. The demands to forgive never cease. This section offers an example of how a sharing of forgiveness can unfold. Feel free to be creative and take some of the other poetic readings and prayers and use them as a source of growth in forgiveness, as we have in this section.

### INDIVIDUAL ASSIGNMENT

Find some quiet space and be alone. Reflect on the situation in your marriage with its good and bad days, its forgiveness and unforgiveness. When you have quieted down and found a comfortable center for yourself, respond to the following:

1. Identify two areas in your marriage that are the most difficult to forgive:

   (a)

   (b)

2. Identify two areas in your marriage where your spouse has trouble forgiving you:

   (a)

   (b)

### INDIVIDUAL ASSIGNMENT

Read to yourself *Winter Warmth* (*The Soul of a Marriage,* pages 105–106). Read it as a prayer of forgiveness and ask God for the strength you need to take a step toward forgiveness. Then be quiet for a time. Let the prayer speak to you about what you want to do. Then respond to the following:

1. Identify where the winter winds of unforgiveness have caused severe alienation for you in your marriage.

2. Identify what you would like to say to your spouse concerning what you want to forgive:

3. Describe the fears you carry about trying to break through the alienation:

4. What do the three words in the prayer (Forgiveness, Forgiveness, Forgiveness) communicate to you about trying again?

5. Write out a brief plan of action about how you are going to proceed with your spouse:

**SHARED ASSIGNMENT**

Present your information to your spouse. Be sure that you give yourselves sufficient time and plenty of space to talk over these matters at length. When the time is right, recite the following prayer together:

Oh God of forgiveness,
help each of us to let go of our grudges,
hurts, pain and emptiness.
Help us remember that You asked us to forgive one
another not just 3 times, but 70 times 7.
Help us to find the way to forgive.
Help us to find the way
in spite of our fears about what may happen to us.
Help us to take the risks, open the doors
and be willing to start all over again when we need to,
then embrace each other.
Give us the spirit of your unconditional love.
Help us to understand
that it is in forgiving
that you are most clearly with us.

# Section 22

## Trying for a Balance

### SHARED ASSIGNMENT

Find some private space and read to yourself pages 73–81 in *The Soul of a Marriage.* These pages explain the difficult time couples have in finding a balance in their marriages. After you have reflected upon the task of achieving a balance for your own marriage, write your responses to the following:

1. In what ways am I different than when I first married?

2. In what ways has my differentness influenced the balance between togetherness and individuality in our marriage?

3. In what ways is my spouse different than in early marriage?

4. Has this impeded or assisted my growth? How?

5. Describe some ways that these changes have changed my view of God:

6. Name a popular song that best describes the dance you and your spouse have been dancing:

## SHARED ASSIGNMENT

Come together and share your answers to these questions. Discuss your similarities and differences. Jointly decide on three ways you want to be more supportive and caring for one another in order to achieve a healthier balance in your marriage:

1.

2.

3.

## SHARED ASSIGNMENT

Jointly recite the *Prayer for an Uneasy Peace* (*The Soul of a Marriage,* page 79) and then sit quietly, allowing the prayer to speak to you.

## SHARED ASSIGNMENT

Jointly select a prayer or a poem from the same section of *The Soul of a Marriage* that speaks to you about your life, and read it to one another. Be quiet for a time.

# Section 23

## Time of Relentless Conflict

### SHARED ASSIGNMENT

Agree to be with each other for 30 minutes and no more. Find a quiet place for yourselves and just be there. Agree that for 30 minutes you will set aside all the pettiness, all the difficulties, all the uncertainty and anger. Even try to agree to *like* one another for this length of time. Give the quiet space an opportunity to speak to you about the fact that you can be peaceful. Allow it to speak to you about some possibilities for your shared lives. Put away all the efforts at problem-solving and simply remain quiet.

### SHARED ASSIGNMENT:

**WIFE:** Read to your husband *In an Unusual Moment* (*The Soul of a Marriage,* page 88). Neither one of you is to say anything for five full minutes. Just be quiet.

### INDIVIDUAL ASSIGNMENT

Now each of you answer *separately* the following questions:

1. The three most convincing reasons to stay in the marriage right now are:

   (a)

   (b)

   (c)

2. If we are to stay together, this remains the most difficult problem we must resolve about ourselves:

## SHARED ASSIGNMENT

*One person at a time,* share your answers with one another, but do not attempt to problem-solve. Try to hear.
Your task is to stay quiet and not answer.

## INDIVIDUAL ASSIGNMENT:

Simply be quiet for a time and pray silently. Each of you turn to *The Soul of a Marriage* pages 87 and 88.

**WIFE:** Pray silently, *Out of Resources.*

**HUSBAND:** Pray silently *Bring Me Nourishment.*

Then simply quiet down for 10 minutes and just *be.*

## SHARED ASSIGNMENT

Turn to page 89 in *The Soul of a Marriage.* Pray together the prayer entitled *Forgiveness* and allow it to sink into your hearts. Simply remain quiet in the presence of one another.

# Section 24

## Breaking Out

**INDIVIDUAL ASSIGNMENT**

Find a quiet space where you can be alone for a time. Be silent and imagine the history of your marriage passing in front of you in all its vivid detail. Try to especially imagine the events through which God has called you to wholeness. Think of the many ways that your lives have changed. Reflect on how these changes have made God more or less real to you. When you have rested a bit and gotten in touch with your own history, answer the following:

1. Describe one or more turning points for your marriage:

2. What internal changes did the turning points bring about in you?

3. Describe three ways that you have discovered new life in your marriage through these turning points:

   (a)

   (b)

   (c)

4. Describe three ways that you came to discover God in the darkness of change in your marriage:

   (a)

   (b)

   (c)

## SHARED ASSIGNMENT

Come together as a couple and share the answers you recorded. Decide where you need more teamwork to bring about a healthier sense of togetherness. Decide how to balance this out with personal freedom. Share it.

## SHARED ASSIGNMENT

**HUSBAND:** Read to your wife *Prayer of Gratitude for the Seasoned Marriage* (*The Soul of a Marriage,* pages 96–97). After you have been quiet for a few moments, share with one another all the ways that you have learned to appreciate each other. Express your gratitude in some fresh and creative way (write a poem, sing a song, wine and dine each other).

## SHARED ASSIGNMENT

Select any of the prayers or poems from pages 96–100 from *The Soul of a Marriage.* Take turns reading aloud to your spouse. After you have read one work, share what prompted you to pick out that particular one.

# Section 25

## Rebirth and Renewal

### SHARED ASSIGNMENT

Smell the roses today. You have been working at marriage for a long time. You have been through a lot together and deserve to savor the rewards of all your hard work. You have reached a level of understanding that few achieve. Take some time of out of your lives and count all the great blessings you have been given.

1. Share with one another the three most important gifts you appreciate about one another:

   (a)

   (b)

   (c)

2. Describe three things you still desire to improve in your marriage:

   (a)

   (b)

   (c)

3. Describe several ways you have learned to see how the light outshines the darkness in your marriage:

### SHARED ASSIGNMENT

**HUSBAND:** read *Variations on Psalm 90* to your wife (*The Soul of a Marriage,* page 107). After resting quietly and reflecting on the meaning of this prayer, share with each other some of the ways that you have gained wisdom of heart in your marriage.

**WIFE:** read to your husband *Variations on Psalm 91* (*The Soul of a Marriage,* page 106). Be quiet for a time and then share the ways that God has been loyal to you for these many years.

# Section 26

# Compassion

## SHARED ASSIGNMENT

Take some time together and just be present to one another. Read your way through the chapter on compassion in *The Soul of a Marriage* (pages 109–121). This will take some time. Discuss what information in the chapter was especially helpful to you. Share what implications and challenges the information holds for your marriage. Converse with one another openly and freely about the following questions.

1. Share an incident from your life where you learned a deep lesson of compassion:

2. Recall one experience with a person in your own history who showed you unconditional love:

3. Describe some ways that this experience helped you understand the phrase, "God is unconditional love":

4. Share some of the difficulties you have in understanding the notion of unconditional love:

5. What have you learned about God's unconditional love from your marriage?

6. Describe for your spouse what it means for you to be more compassionate toward one another:

7. Share with each other some areas in your marriage where you need to become more compassionate:

8. Decide on a concrete plan of action to become more compassionate with each other and write down three elements of this plan:

   (a)

   (b)

   (c)

## SHARED ASSIGNMENT

Decide who is going to read. Then read to your spouse *Prayer to Be Read at Graveside* (*The Soul of a Marriage,* pages 120–121). Be quiet for a time and let the feelings speak to you about your value to one another. Discuss how you will treat each other differently from this moment on:

# *Section 27*

# The Quest for Authenticity

## INDIVIDUAL ASSIGNMENT

Take some time away from each other and read for yourself pages 122–126 from *The Soul of a Marriage.* These pages explore the integration of a healthy marital spirituality. Even though some of this material is a bit technical, it is helpful for understanding how a healthy soulfullness develops. After you have taken enough time to reflect on this information, respond to the following:

1. Describe three strengths you bring to your marriage:

   (a)

   (b)

   (c)

2. Describe three strengths your spouse brings to your marriage:

   (a)

   (b)

   (c)

## SHARED ASSIGNMENT

Come back together as a couple and compare your answers. Spend some time discussing your respective strengths and weaknesses. Now jointly respond to the following:

1. Recall an incident(s) when you began to believe in your own competence as a couple:

2. Describe several ways that you will carry the experience of competence into your future together:

3. Describe several ways that you will support one another in this endeavor:

# Section 28

## Learning to Surrender

### SHARED ASSIGNMENT

Sit together for a period of time and read page 127 of *The Soul of a Marriage* on the process of surrender. Share with one another why this process is so essential for the development of a healthy marriage.

### INDIVIDUAL ASSIGNMENT

Answer these questions:

1. Describe what has been the easiest matter for you to surrender in this marriage:

2. Describe what has been the most difficult matter to surrender in your marriage:

### SHARED ASSIGNMENT

Share the results of your individual answers to these questions. Listen to one another about the joys and the difficulties in learning to surrender. Listen to how your spouse has been supportive or non-supportive in this process. Respond as a couple to the following task.

1. Jointly construct a plan of action about how you will support one another from now on in the process of surrender and write down three elements of this plan:

   (a)

   (b)

   (c)

# Section 29

## Listening to Others

**SHARED ASSIGNMENT**

Take time together and read through pages 127–128 in *The Soul of a Marriage.* These pages relate to listening to others as a component of an enriched marital spirituality. Now do the following exercises together:

1. Discuss with one another several ways that you learned to listen to others, and have been enriched by the experience:

2. Explain to each other why it is sometimes difficult for you to learn from others.

3. Jointly agree on a concrete plan of action whereby you are going to open up listening to others and write down three elements of this plan:

   (a)

   (b)

   (c)

# Section 30

# Learning to Take Risks

## INDIVIDUAL ASSIGNMENT

Sit alone and read through pages 128–129 from *The Soul of a Marriage* about taking risks in a marriage. Now relate to the following tasks:

1. Describe three ways that your marriage is dead-centered from the lack of risk-taking:

   (a)

   (b)

   (c)

2. Describe three ways that you have tried to take some risks but your spouse has not cooperated:

   (a)

   (b)

   (c)

## SHARED ASSIGNMENT

Sit with your spouse and share your responses with one another. Be sure to take the time to hear what has been lacking in your marriage. After you have heard one another, do the following together:

1. Develop a joint plan of action to take one new risk each week:

2. Set the schedule for the next month so that you make sure you follow through on your plan of action:

# Section 31

# Living in the Here and Now

## INDIVIDUAL ASSIGNMENT

Take your individual space and read pages 129–131 in *The Soul of a Marriage.* As you read about mindfulness, take note of what it means in finding a richer marriage. You will find below three exercises in mindfulness from Thich Nhat Hanh's book, *The Miracle of Mindfulness* (Boston: Beacon Press, 1975). Set aside 15 to 45 minutes to be alone in a very quiet space of your own and do one of the exercises.

*Mindfulness While Making Tea*

> Prepare a pot of tea to serve a guest or to drink by yourself. Do each movement slowly, in mindfulness. Do not let one detail of your movements go by without being mindful of it. Know that your hand lifts the pot by its handle. Know that you are pouring the fragrant warm tea into the cup. Follow each step in mindfulness. Breathe gently and more deeply than usual. Take hold of your breath if your mind strays.

*A Slow-Motion Bath*

> Allow yourself 30 to 45 minutes to take a bath. Don't hurry for even one second. From the moment you prepare the bathwater to the moment you put on clean clothes, let every motion be light and slow. Be attentive of every movement. Place your attention on every part of your body, without discrimination or fear. Be mindful of each stream of water on your body. By the time you've finished, your mind should be as peaceful and light as your body. Follow your breath. Think of yourself as being in a clean and fragrant lotus pond in the summer.

*A Meditation on Yourself*

> Sit in a dark room by yourself, or alone by a river at night, or anywhere else where there is solitude. Begin to take hold of your breath. Give rise to the thought, "I will use my finger to point at myself," and then instead of pointing at your body, point away in the opposite direction. Contemplate seeing yourself outside of your bodily form. Contemplate seeing your bodily form present before you—in the trees, the grass and leaves, the river. Be mindful that you are in the universe and the universe is in you: if the universe is, you are; if you are, the universe is. There is no birth. There is no death. There is no coming. There is no going. Maintain the half-smile. Take hold of your breath. Contemplate for 10 to 20 minutes.

When you have finished, just enjoy the peacefulness. It cannot help but benefit you, and your marriage as well. Note: There are a number of captivating exercises like this in *The Miracle of Mindfulness.* If you want to explore the art of mindfulness further, consult this work.

# Section 32

## Learning to Laugh

### INDIVIDUAL ASSIGNMENT

Sit together as a couple and give yourself plenty of time to talk. Read together page 131 from *The Soul of a Marriage.* Relate as a couple to the following:

1. Describe to one another the three funniest episodes of your entire married life:

   (a)

   (b)

   (c)

2. Share with one another what you each learned through the experience:

3. What has blocked your ability to laugh together more frequently?

4. Construct a concrete plan where you will seek more opportunities for laughter in your life.

# Section 33

# Accepting Your Own Pettiness

## INDIVIDUAL ASSIGNMENT

Find your private space and read *The Soul of a Marriage* pages 131–132 concerning one's own pettiness. Take some time to reflect on your foibles and relate to the following:

1. Describe the three most petty things you do in your marriage:

   (a)

   (b)

   (c)

2. Describe the three most petty things your spouse does in your marriage:

   (a)

   (b)

   (c)

3. Describe how both your own and your spouse's pettiness cloud the atmosphere of your marriage:

## SHARED ASSIGNMENT

Sit with your spouse and share the results of your reflections on pettiness. Try to hear each other and be open to the ways that small things have impeded progress in your marriage. Relate to the following.

1. Construct a joint plan of action about one petty matter each of you is going to drop this week:

# Section 34

## Efforts to Change One Another

### INDIVIDUAL ASSIGNMENT

Find a quiet space for yourself and read *The Soul of a Marriage,* page 132. Reflect on all the efforts, all the arguments, all the difficulties that have flowed from trying to change each other's behavior. Relate to the following:

1. Describe three "quirks" in your partner that you have attempted to change but have not been able to achieve:

   (a)

   (b)

   (c)

### SHARED ASSIGNMENT

Sit with your spouse and share your responses. Take time and discuss in detail your efforts as well as your failures. Relate as a couple to these two questions:

1. Did you become aware that what you are trying to change in your spouse also exists in you?

2. What percentage of your time and energy is dedicated to changing your spouse rather than yourself?

### SHARED ASSIGNMENT

**WIFE:** read to your husband *Back on Track* from *The Soul of a Marriage,* page 98. After reading it, both of you be quiet for a time and decide what to do with the information.

**HUSBAND:** read to your spouse *Letting Go and Feeling Good* from *The Soul of a Marriage,* pages 99–100. After reading it, both remain quiet.

# Section 35

## A Vital Sexuality

### SHARED ASSIGNMENT

Sit closely together and read the section in *The Soul of a Marriage* on a vital sexuality (pages 132–133). Be quiet for a time, hold each others' hands, and reflect on the many sexual experiences you have had together. Let the experiences speak to you about how desirable you are and how these experiences have sensitized you to be more loving. After some quiet conversation about these matters, relate to the following.

1. Share with one another what a vital sexuality means at this stage in your marriage:

2. Describe to one another when you feel the most sexually fulfilled:

3. Share with one another when you feel the most empty:

4. Describe some of the ways that your own sexual experiences have helped you understand the passionate love of God:

5. Share with one another when your sexual experiences open out into an experience of God:

6. Share what you would like to do to become more sensitive to one another:

# Section 36

## Savoring Trust

### SHARED ASSIGNMENT

Sit together as a couple and read the brief description of the vital and deep trust that is so important to a marital spirituality (*The Soul of a Marriage,* page 133). Share with each other whatever seems appropriate at this moment in your lives. Relate it to the ways that trust has deepened. If there are problems of mistrust that still linger, identify what needs to be resolved if trust is to mature. End your discussion by making three resolutions concerning actions that will help you each with a deepening trust:

1.

2.

3.

# *Section 37*

# Learning to Live With Paradox

## INDIVIDUAL ASSIGNMENT

Find your separate spaces and read the section from *The Soul of a Marriage* on learning to live with paradox (pages 134–136). Reflect on the many changes in your marriage. Recount the "*soul of a marriage*" you have lived through and the ways that God has become more real for you through them. Relate to the following:

1. Describe three ways that the darkness became light in your marriage:

    (a)

    (b)

    (c)

2. Describe three ways that the light became darkness in your marriage:

    (a)

    (b)

    (c)

## SHARED ASSIGNMENT

Sit with your spouse and share your answers with one another. Share, especially, the lessons learned from trying to find God in the darkness. Share what the surprises were as well as the disappointments. Relate to the following:

1. What changes in attitude do you both need in order to see the light instead of the darkness in your marriage?

# Section 38

## The Place of Prayer

### SHARED ASSIGNMENT

Sit as a couple and read together the last section of *The Soul of a Marriage* (pages 136–end). Be quiet for a time and find your center. Discuss the following:

1. What constitutes the deepest and most genuine prayers in your marriage?

2. Where do you find prayer lacking?

3. Construct a practical plan so that prayer becomes an integral part of your life:

### INDIVIDUAL ASSIGNMENT:

Each of you take 30 minutes and write a prayer for the other person. It can be a prayer of praise for the rich gifts that have been given in your marriage. It can be a prayer of asking God to listen to your needs. It can be any kind of prayer as long as it expresses the heart of the two of you. When you are finished, read it to your spouse. Give each other a written copy to keep and pray. Take your prayers home and post them in a place where they can be recited each day.

### A FINAL WORD

We have enjoyed being with you as you have explored your marriage together. Thank you for using our workbook. Go back to the exercises as often as you want and use them to revitalize your marriage. Apply your creativity in some fresh ways if you choose. We both wish you the best as your journey continues and you open yourselves to the loving God who brought you together.

*Patrick J. and Claudette M. McDonald*